This annual belongs to

Published by Parragon in 2011
Distributed by D.C. Thomson Annuals Ltd
D.C. Thomson Annuals Ltd
Courier Buildings
2 Albert Square
Dundee
DD1 9QJ

© Ludorum plc 2011
www.chuggington.com

ISBN 978-1-84535-457-2

Printed in Italy

CONTENTS

Packed with traintastic activities!

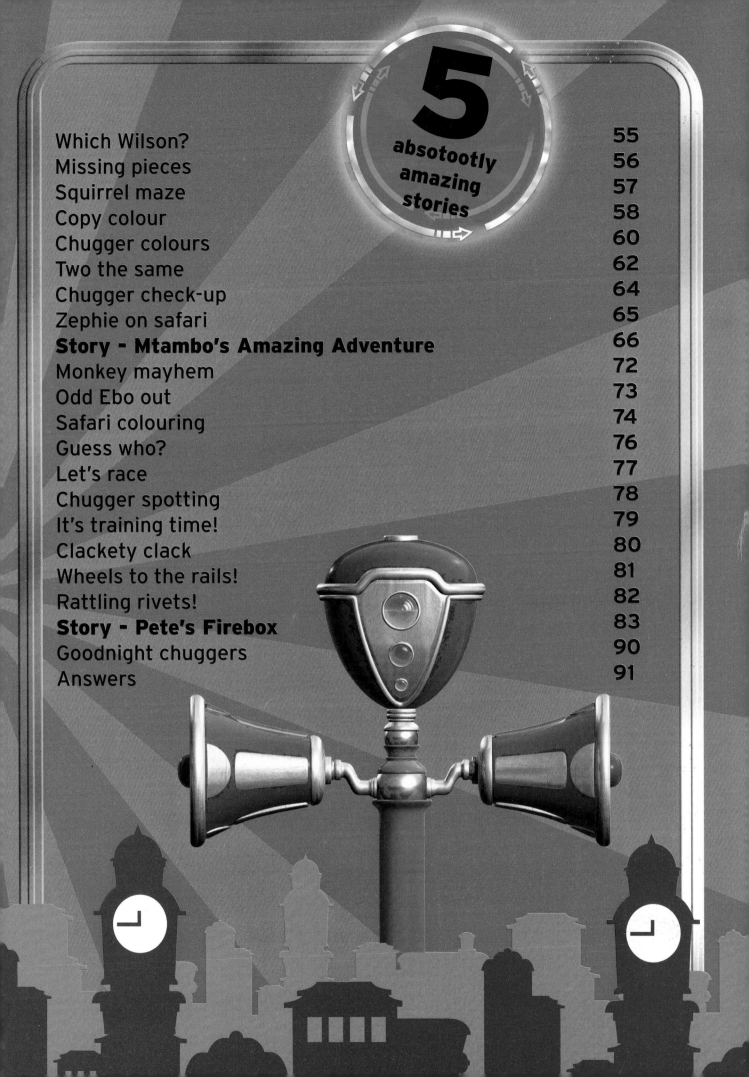

5 absotootly amazing stories

The trainees

Brewster, Koko and Wilson are the three trainees.

Wilson

Koko

Brewster

Wilson is an excitable red trainee who is always ready to learn new things.

Koko is a fast green trainee who loves to discover new places.

Brewster is a brave blue trainee who likes to help with strong loads.

It's training time!

Draw lines to connect each missing part to the picture of the trainees.

Meet the chuggers!

The chuggers of Chuggington are all different shapes and sizes.

Wilson

Koko

Brewster

Dunbar

Frostini

Mtambo

Calley

Irving

Harrison

Emery

Chatsworth

Hodge

Action Chugger

Old Puffer Pete

Olwin

Zephie

What would your chugger name be?

Create your own chugger

What would you look like as a chugger?
Draw yourself as a chugger on the tracks!

How many horns, headlights and wheels would you have?

Choo choo!

Can you help Koko count all the chuggers?
Point to each chugger you find and say,
"Choo choo!"
Then write over the correct number of chuggers.

Odd one out

Which picture of Harrison and Old Puffer Pete is the odd one out?

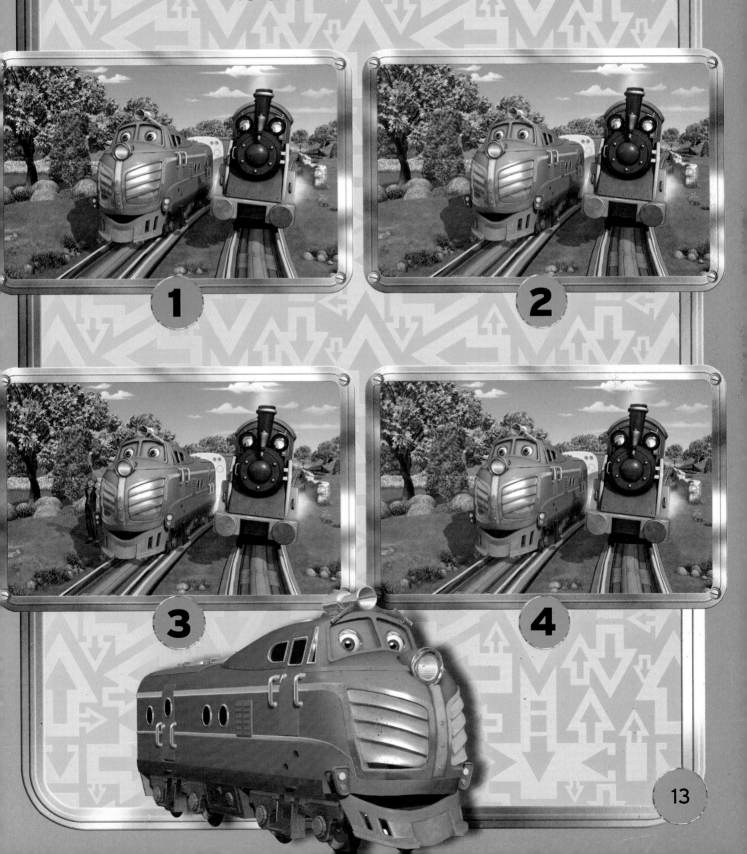

Training Time Harrison

Vee had a very special announcement. She needed a chugger to pull the royal carriage.

"I want to do it!" Wilson said excitedly.

"But we're just trainees," Koko said. "Vee's not going to let us do it!"

When Harrison heard about the special job, he thought he should be the one pulling the royal carriage. In his rush to get back to the depot, he raced through a red light. In surprise Olwin jumped off the rails.

"Sorry, Olwin!" Harrison called as he dashed away.

Then Harrison caught up with Chatsworth, who wanted to pull the royal carriage as well.
"The track ahead's blocked!" Harrison cheekily advised. He wanted Chatsworth to turnaround so he could get to the depot first.

"The Prince of Buffertonia is visiting for a royal tour," Vee told Harrison when he arrived at the depot. "Pete will teach you what to do."
"I'm not a trainee you know," Harrison said, chuckling and rolling his eyes.

Harrison wanted to speed up Pete's practice tour.
"Rattling rivets! Harrison, you're going too fast! The prince won't be able to see anything," Pete puffed.
"Nonsense," Harrison replied, wanting to do the tour his way.

"You didn't sound your horn before you went over that crossing!" Pete called, as Harrison tried to take a short cut.
"The route is set, Harrison. It's tradition."

When Vee heard about the practice tour she had an idea.

"I suggest you join the trainees and refresh your memory of the rules of the rails. Off to the training yard, Harrison."

"I rule the rails! Watch and learn, trainees." Harrison boasted when he got to the training yard. Zipping around the tracks and ignoring all the signs, he showed off with dangerous wheelies and single rail riding. The trainees watched excitedly.

"That was the most perfecto thing I've ever seen. I'm going to try it!" Wilson shouted. But Wilson lost his balance and fell off the rails with a big crash.

"Oh bumpers!"

"This is all my fault. I should have set a better example for you," Harrison said, feeling very ashamed as Calley lifted Wilson back onto the rails.

"I'll do better. I've got into some bad habits. Dunbar, it's training time!"

So Harrison practised checking for signs, looking both ways at crossings and riding slow and steady on the rails. "Thanks for getting me back on track," he told Wilson.

Everyone watched proudly as Harrison carefully pulled the royal carriage along the rails.

"Go, Harrison, go! Three honks for the prince," Koko called.

"Hooray!" all the watching chuggers cheered.

"HOORAY, FOR HARRISON!"

Which track?

Which track takes Harrison to the training yard?

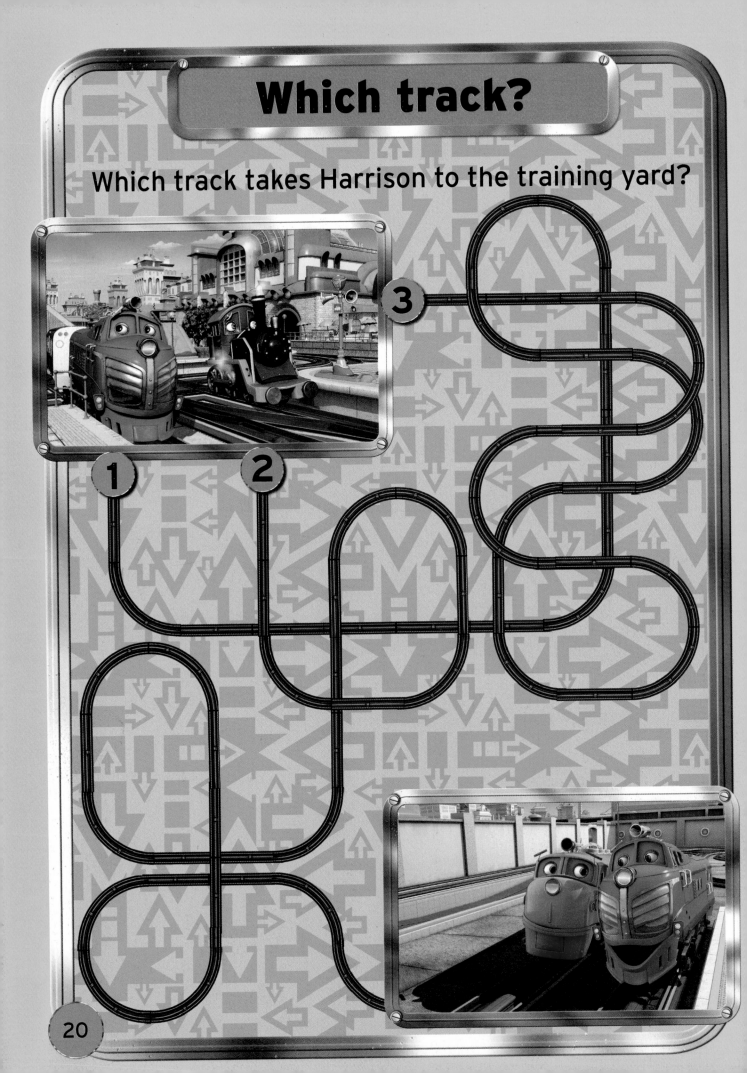

Brewster

Honking horns!

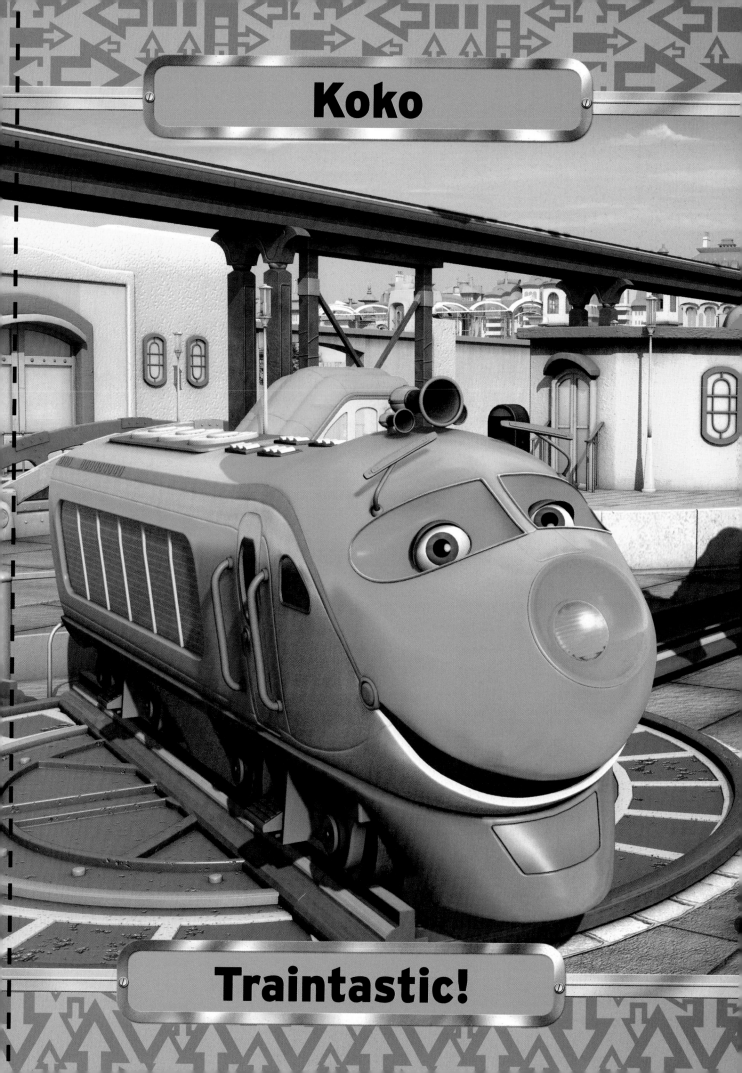

Koko

Traintastic!

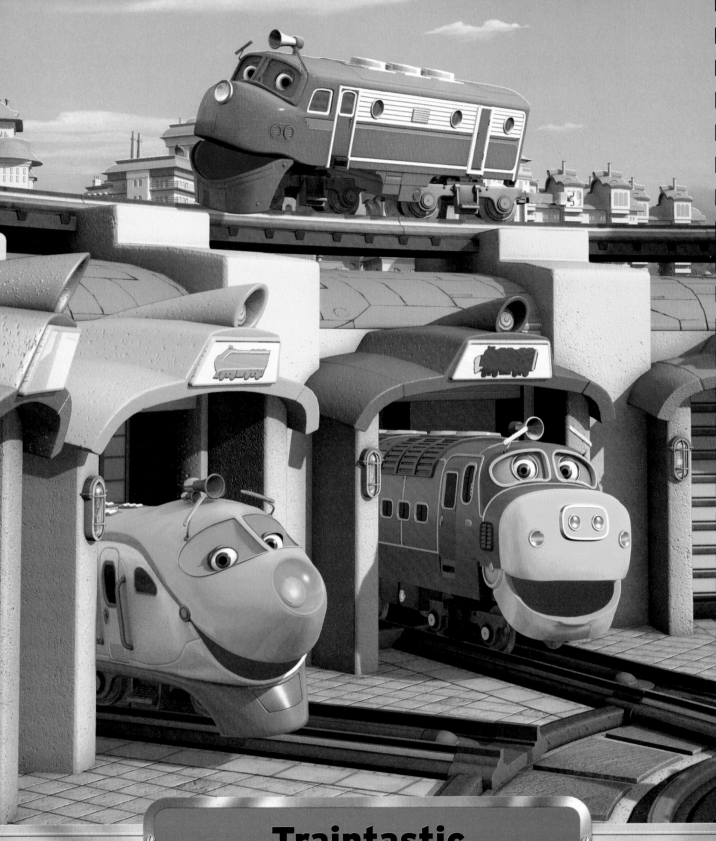

Wheels to the rails!

Traintastic

It's training time!

The trainees are practising new moves. Tick the trainee that comes next in each pattern.

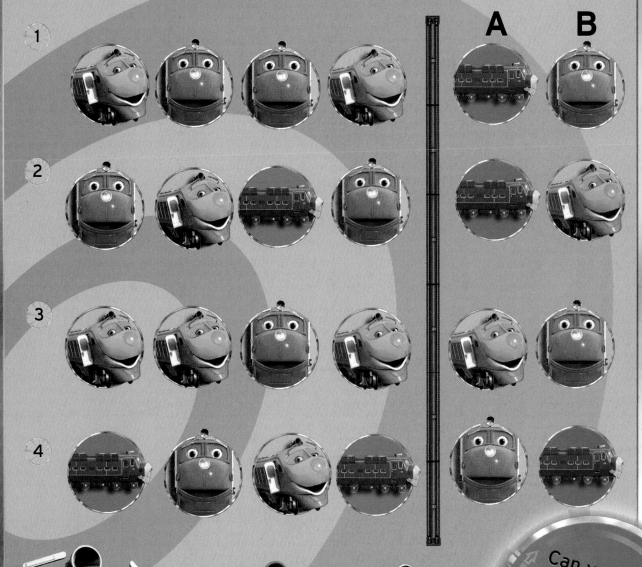

Clackety clack quiz

Which trainee are you?
Circle your answer to each question, then turn
over to find out which trainee you are most like!

1.   What's your favourite
     phrase?

A)   Chugga chugga,
     choo choo!
B)   Honking horns!
C)   Let's ride the rails!

2.   What colour clothes
     do you wear the most?

A)   Green.
B)   Blue.
C)   Red.

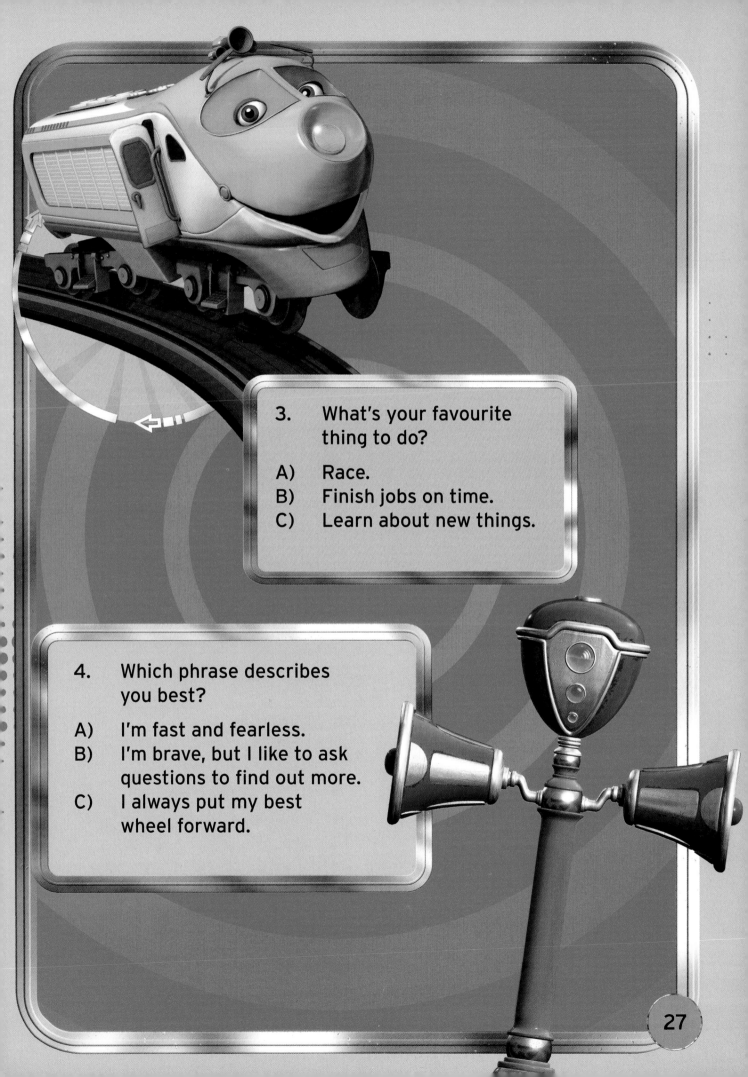

3. **What's your favourite thing to do?**

A) Race.
B) Finish jobs on time.
C) Learn about new things.

4. **Which phrase describes you best?**

A) I'm fast and fearless.
B) I'm brave, but I like to ask questions to find out more.
C) I always put my best wheel forward.

Which trainee are you?

Mostly A's

You're most like Koko! Koko is a fearless electric engine who's fast on the tracks. She likes the colours green and purple. Koko loves to say "Traintastic!" especially when she wins a race.

Mostly B's

You're most like Brewster! Brewster is a brave diesel engine who's great at pulling heavy loads. Brewster likes to ask questions about a job before it starts, and he likes the colours blue and yellow. Brewster's favourite phrase is "Honking horns!"

Mostly C's

You're most like Wilson! Wilson is a lively multi-function trainee. Wilson enjoys learning new things and tries his best on every job. He prefers the colour red and his favourite phrase is "Let's ride the rails!"

Chugger height chart

Chuggers come in all different heights. Circle the chugger who is the smallest and draw a rectangle around the largest chugger.

A rectangle

A circle

Now draw a picture of yourself next to Wilson. Are you bigger or smaller than Wilson?

Puffer Pete's Big Party

One morning, the chuggers gathered around Vee to hear some important news.

"Tomorrow is the anniversary of Old Puffer Pete's first day in Chuggington, 150 years ago!" she said.

"The mayor would like us to put on a big show to celebrate, but first we have to distract Pete so it will be a surprise."

Vee asked Pete to go on several jobs so he would be away all day.

"Rattling rivets!" Pete said. "Can anyone come to help?"
"Can't stop!" Brewster puffed by.

"In a rush," Koko called.
"I'm...busier than a...busy bee." Wilson panted past.

As soon as Pete puffed away through the tunnel, Dunbar told Wilson, Koko and Brewster that they were to be the stars of Pete's big show.
"Traintastic," shouted Koko.
"We're going to be stars!" gasped Wilson.

31

At the training yard, the trainees practised their moves for the show. It was hard work keeping their wheels together.

"Koko, you're going too fast!" grumbled Wilson.

"Am not! You're a slow coach!" Koko shouted back, as Brewster took the wrong track.

Suddenly, Brewster and Wilson crashed into each other.

"Honking horns! Look where you're going will you?" Brewster said.

Dunbar sighed. He didn't think his engine could take much more of this.

"Oh bumpers!" Wilson said as he made another mistake.

"We might have to cancel the show," Dunbar told Olwin, who was watching them practise.

"Oh no!" Koko cried, "We can't let everyone down!"

So the trainees sneaked out in the middle of the night to practise their moves.

"We need to roll together," Koko said. "Let's count out loud: **1**-2-3-4, **2**-2-3-4..."

"...**3**-2-3-4, **4**-2-3-4..." Brewster and Wilson joined in.

"We're doing it! Go, trainees, go!" Koko said excitedly.

In the morning, Vee called Pete to the training yard.

"Surprise!" the waiting chuggers shouted.

"Rattling rivets!" Pete said happily, as Wilson, Koko and Brewster rolled into place.

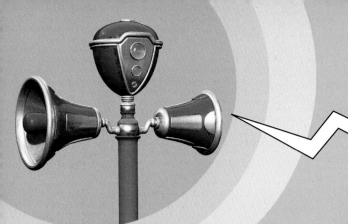

PETE, 150 YEARS AGO TODAY, YOUR WHEELS FIRST RODE THE RAILS IN CHUGGINGTON. SO WE WANT TO THANK YOU WITH A BIG SHOW!

"The kindest chugger you could ever meet, is our great friend, Old Puffer Pete!

We're trainees and he teaches us a lot. Huffing and puffing, giving everything he's got!" The trainees sang, gliding in time to the music.

"No matter what we do, he never blows a gasket. We're here to tell you, Puffer Pete is traintastic!

So chuggers please, join us as we say, Old Puffer Pete, Happy anniverssssssssssssary!" They cheered, as a flatbed car rolled into view, carrying a surprise for Pete.

A curtain dropped and a model of Pete was revealed.

"Smashing!" Pete cried. Fireworks whizzed and burst overhead.

"Well done chuggers!" Dunbar said. Everyone cheered.

"Only another 50 years and we can celebrate my 200th anniversary!" Pete said, smiling.

"Oh bumpers! We better start practising!" Wilson laughed.

Colouring fun

Colour in Old Puffer Pete!

Can you puff like Pete?

Who lives where?

Draw lines to connect each animal in Chuggington to its home.

A

1

B

2

C

3

D

4

Emergency rescue

Calley is Chuggington's emergency rescue chugger. Tick the correct picture for emergency steps 1, 2, 3!

1. Push the emergency button.

2. Don't panic.

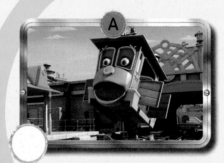

3. Listen out for approaching chuggers and honk your horns three times.

Can you make a noise like a horn?

Toot, Toot!

Chugger colouring

Dunbar and Irving have different jobs. Dunbar teaches the trainees and Irving collects rubbish and recycling. Colour in Dunbar and Irving!

What's your favourite way to help at home?

Rubbish to recycle

There are lots of things to recycle in Chuggington.
Draw lines to connect the pictures to their labels.

Grass

Rubbish

Wood

Rocks

Paper

Metal

How many?

How many of each thing does each chugger have?

Dunbar

Calley

Mtambo

Frostini

Make your own trainee name badge for your
bedroom door! Ask an adult to help you cut out
the different shapes and stick them to your badge.

Dot to dot

Join the dots 1-10 to complete Vee,
then colour her in!

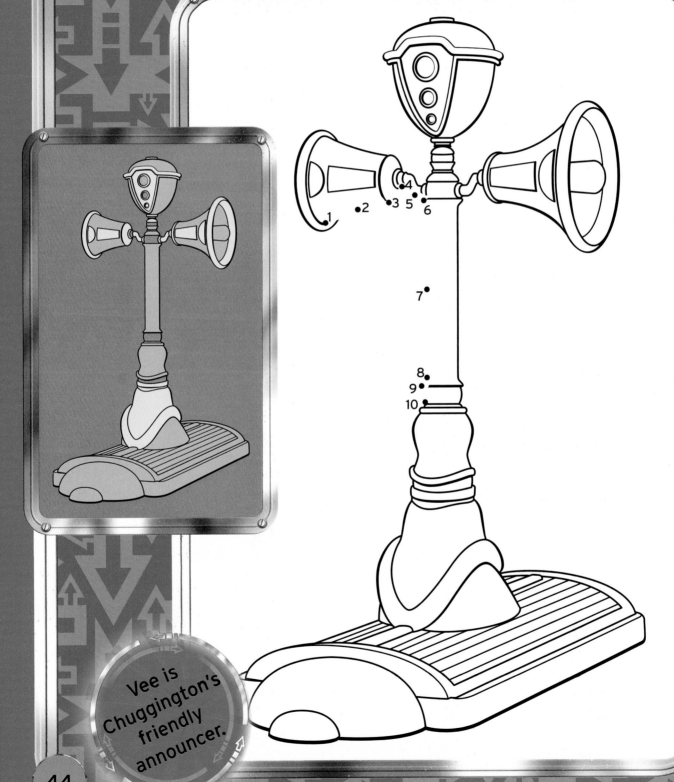

Vee is Chuggington's friendly announcer.

44

Traintastic puzzle

Ask an adult to cut out the squares, then mix up the pieces. See if you can make this picture and the picture on the other side!

Traintastic puzzle

Ask an adult to cut out the squares, then mix up the pieces and see if you can make this picture, and the picture on the other side!

Spot the difference

Can you spot the five differences between these two pictures? Colour in a ticket when you spot each difference.

Frostini's Fruit Fandango

Wilson was excited to be Frostini's assistant at the ice cream factory. "If Frostini's pleased, you'll earn a Good Helper Badge," Vee said. "Wahay! I'll be the most helpful helper ever, ever, ever."

"You're just in time to see my special creation for the mayor's banquet tonight," Frostini told Wilson.
   "Wowzer!"

"The great Frostini presents Chuggtastic Chewy Cheesecake!" Frostini announced.
   "Oh dear, the mayor's wife can't have cheese," the mayor's assistant said.
   "What a disaster!" Frostini cried. Time to start again.

Frostini started to work on his new flavour.
"I choose the ingredients and the mixer blends them together,"
he told Wilson, looking at the yummy food in the factory.

"Too bland...too sweet...this is a disaster!" Frostini
complained, sniffing different ingredients for the new flavour.
"I must speak to Vee."

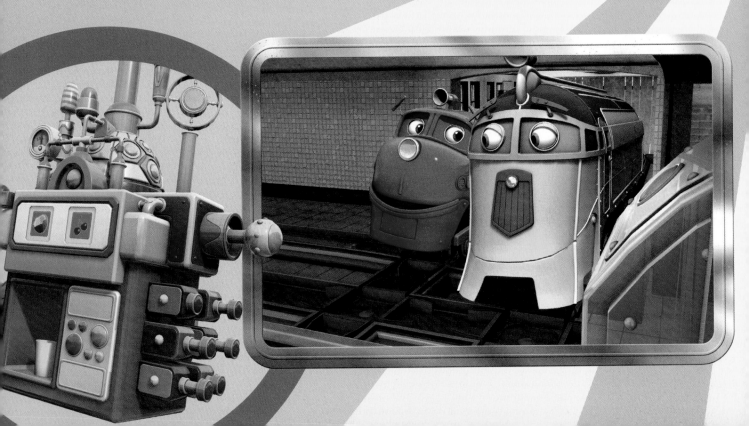

Wilson thought he could help Frostini by trying different mixtures himself.

"Mix toffee and tuna fish!" he told the mixer loudly. "Mix banana and baked beans!" he shouted excitedly as the mixer started to shake. "Tuna fish and toothpaste!" Wilson yelled.

Suddenly the mixer exploded, covering Wilson in ice cream.

Just then, Frostini came back.

"I have to come up with a masterpiece and you have broken my mixer!" he cried.

"Clean up at the chuggwash, then go to the Safari Park to do my ice cream round," Frostini told Wilson.

"I'm really sorry," Wilson said, chugging away.

At the Safari Park, the monkeys were throwing fruit at each other. "Naughty monkeys!" Wilson cried as different fruit flew through the air, covering him with a fruity mess.

Back at the depot, Frostini suddenly smelled something fresh, fruity and fantastico. It was Wilson on his way to the chuggwash again!
"I smell the recipe of the century!" Frostini gasped, zooming to catch up with Wilson.

"Stop!" Frostini shouted, stopping Wilson before he washed off all the fruit. "What is that delicious smell?"

"Well, there's bananas, pineapple, mangoes, kiwi, papaya, peach..." Wilson listed.

Following Wilson's list, Frostini created a new flavour. The mayor's assistant loved it.

"What do you call it?"

"It's Frostini's Fruit Fandango, co-created by Wilson. Wilson you have been an excellent assistant and earned your Helper Badge."

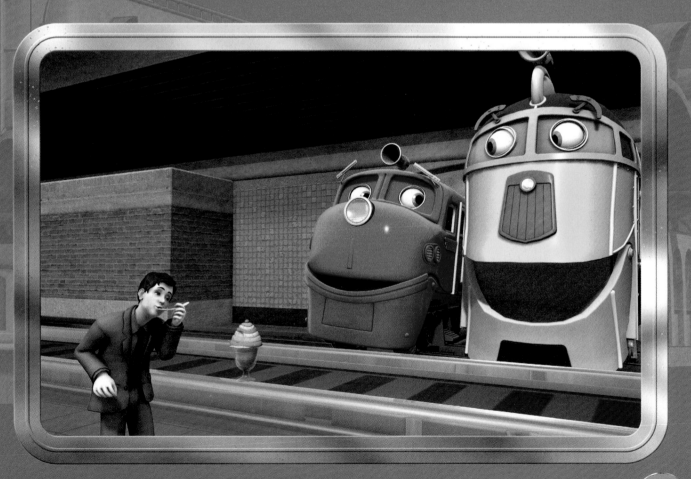

"PERFECTO!"

Ice cream colours

Draw lines to connect each ice cream to the correct colour.

Red

Yellow

Green

Blue

Purple

1   2   3   4   5

Which Wilson?

Which picture of Wilson is the odd one out?

Missing pieces

Draw lines to connect the missing pieces to the scene, then tick the chuggers in the picture.

Squirrel maze

Good chuggers are always willing to help. Can you help Koko make a bridge for the squirrels by following the squirrels through the maze?

Start

Finish

Copy colour

Action Chugger is a flying super-hero chugger.
Use the grid lines to help you
copy and colour his picture!

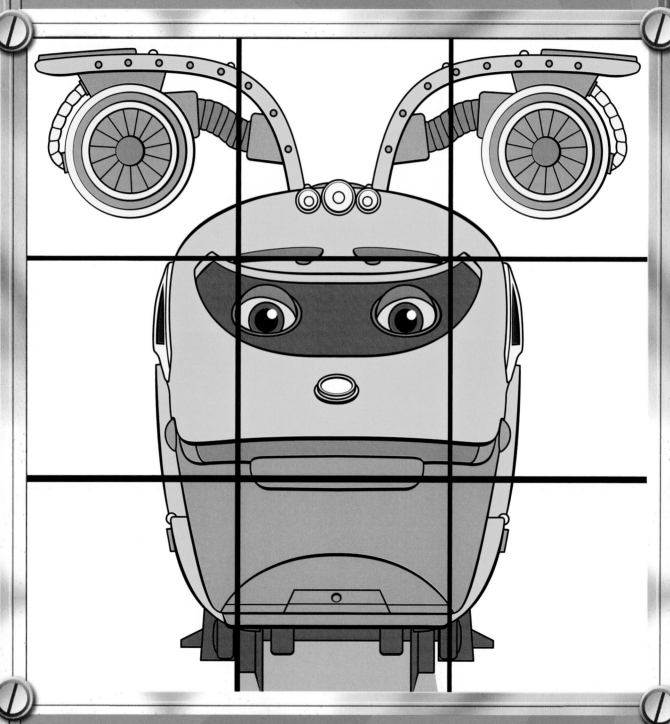

If you were a super-hero what would your special power be?

Chugger colours

The chuggers are all different colours.
Tick the correct colours for each chugger!

Koko

Wilson

Brewster

Olwin

Old Puffer Pete

Calley

Two the same

Can you find two pictures of Brewster that look the same? Circle the two that match!

A

B

C

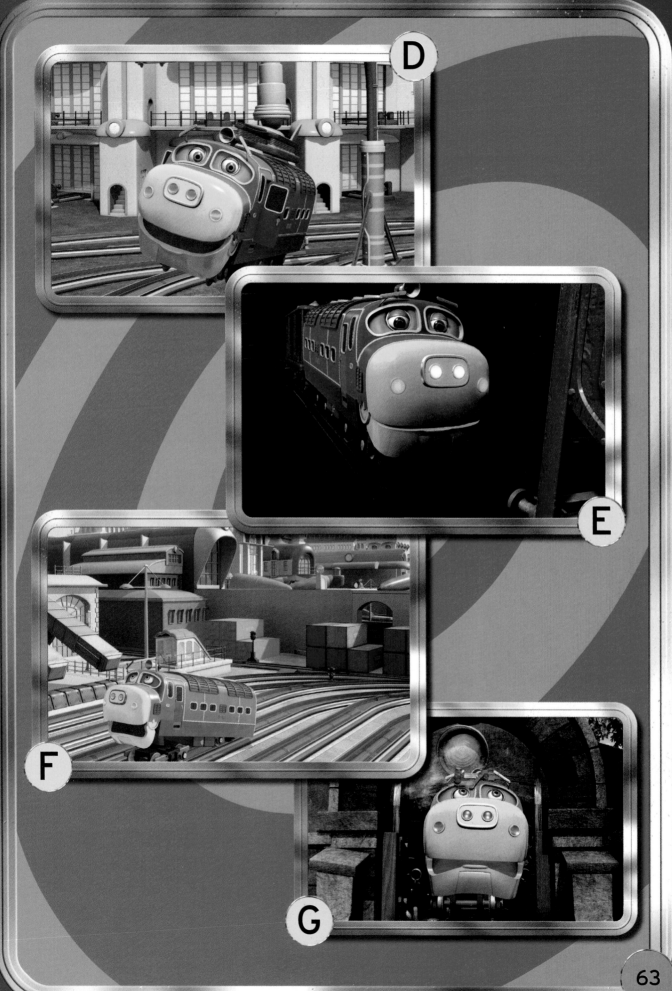

D

E

F

G

63

Chugger check-up

Old Puffer Pete is having a chug scan. The scan sweeps over Pete to find if anything needs fixing. Which close-up is not in the big picture?

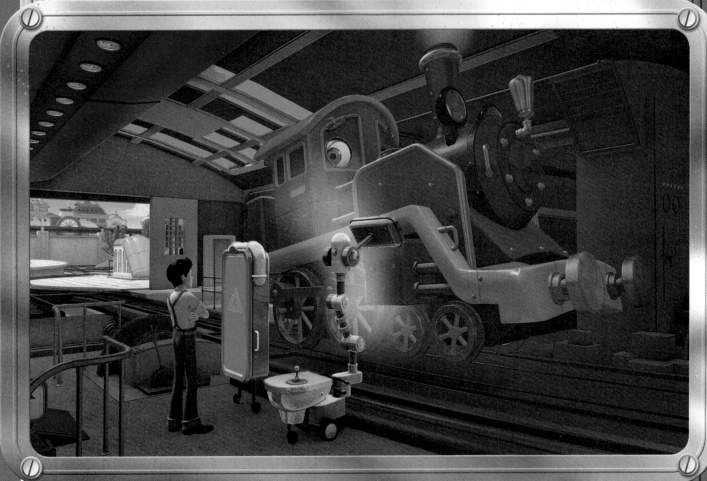

Zephie on safari

Zephie is excited about helping at the Safari Park. Which animal will she look after first, second, third and fourth?

Mtambo's Amazing Adventure

The trainees asked Mtambo to tell them a story.
"Once I got lost in the desert and – "
"Along came a camel that guided you out," they finished.
They knew all his stories!

The next morning, Vicky asked Mtambo to collect a Gigantic Crested Lizard from the docks.
"A new adventure! I'll have a new story to tell!"

Koko, Wilson and Brewster were trying their wheels at filling a tanker car with water. Wilson practised with the hose first.
"Watch out! I'm an elephant!" he shouted, splashing Koko with water.

"I'm going to collect a Gigantic Crested Lizard. It's a huge beast. It will be quite an adventure!" Mtambo told Ebo, the elephant at the Safari Park. "Sorry Mtambo," Vicky said. "Can you take a gentleman on a tour instead?"

Vee asked if one of the trainees could go to the docks instead of Mtambo. "Honking horns. That's a job for a strong chugger. I'll go," Brewster said excitedly.

Meanwhile, Mtambo was taking a man called Freddy on a tour of the Safari Park. He was disappointed he couldn't go to the docks.

"Ebo likes to make a splash," he said, when Ebo sprayed a trunkful of water at them.

"I could use a chugger like you on my jungle adventures," Freddy told Mtambo.

"If I went to the jungle, I would come back with new stories to tell..." Mtambo said to the monkeys.

While Freddy was away, one of the monkeys grabbed his camera and ran away with it.

"You cheeky monkey! Give it back!" Mtambo called, racing after him.

Mtambo zoomed past the giraffes and into the elephant park, following the monkey as he jumped and ran around the animals, taking their picture.

Finally the monkey stopped. Jumping onto Ebo's back, he slid down his trunk, snapping a surprised photo of the elephant. Ebo quickly threw the camera back to Mtambo.

When Brewster arrived at the Safari Park with the lizard, everyone gathered around to see the giant animal. Vicky opened the cage and they were all surprised at how small it was!

That evening, Mtambo told the trainees about his amazing adventure with the cheeky monkey and the camera.

"The next time I want to roam, I'll look for an adventure here at home!" he laughed.

"TRAINTASTIC!"

Monkey mayhem

How many monkeys can you spot at
the Safari Park?
Write in the number that you find.

Odd Ebo out

Which Ebo is the odd one out?

Safari colouring

Colour in Mtambo, Brewster and Wilson at the Safari Park!

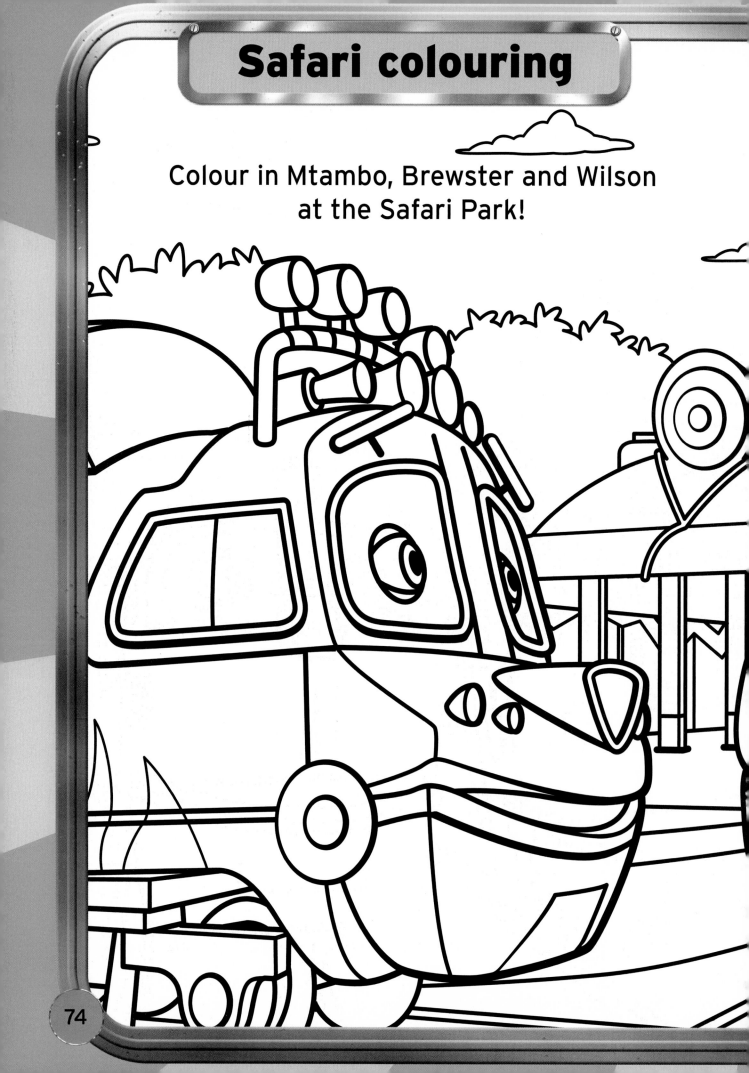

Guess who?

Who is chugging along the tracks? Look at all the close-up pictures and circle the correct chugger!

Let's race

The trainees have just raced around the depot. Join the different coloured dots together to find out who came first, second and third!

"On your tracks, set, go!"

Brewster's number
is blue.

Koko's number
is purple.

Wilson's number
is red.

Chugger spotting

Can you spot Irving?

Where's Calley?

Do you see Brewster?

Find Action Chugger!

It's training time!

Traintastic!

Wheels to the rails!

Rattling rivets!

Circle the chugger phrases where all the words begin with the same letter.

Chugga, chugga, choo, choo!

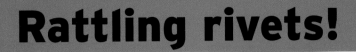

Have no fear, Action Chugger is here!

Wheels to the rails!

Rattling rivets!

Absotootly amazing!

83

Pete's Firebox

Old Puffer Pete was puffing a lot more than usual. All the smoke was making him cough.

"I think you'd better get a check-up." Olwin coughed through a big cloud of smoke.

Pete chugged into the repair shed with a puff, a bang and a clang!

"Ohh! That doesn't sound good," Morgan said, coughing under the cloud.

The chug scan found that Pete's firebox was broken.

"It'll take weeks to get a new firebox specially made," Morgan said.

"RATTLING RIVETS!"

Calley was teaching the trainees when Vee asked her to tow Pete to his roundhouse. So the trainees decided to play hide and seek in Old Chuggington. "Let's ride the rails!" Wilson called as they chugged away.

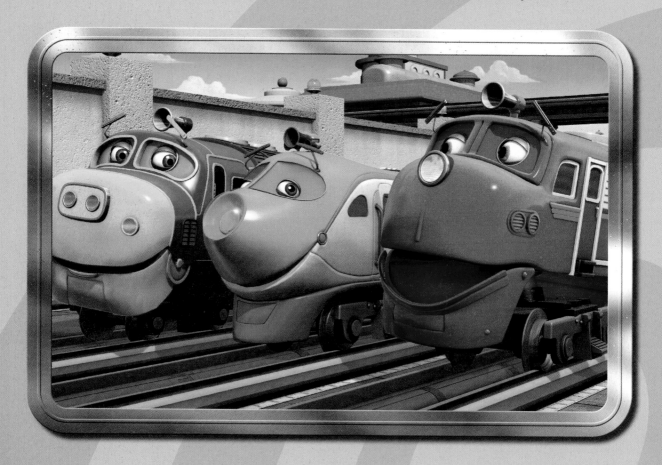

"Can't find Koko," Koko said as she whizzed around Old Chuggington. "One, two, three... ready or not here I come!" Wilson shouted, heading off to find his friends.

"They'll never find me in here," whispered Brewster when he spotted an old dark shed. He jumped as lots of spare parts fell onto his roof with a loud crash.

"Honking horns!"

"Found you!" Wilson and Koko called, laughing as Brewster shook and wobbled his bumpers to get all the parts off.

When Pete found out about the old parts shed he asked Morgan if Zephie could take them to Old Chuggington. Everyone started searching for a firebox for Pete.

Olwin asked Vee if there was any news from Old Chuggington.

"Poor Pete. I hope they find that firebox," Olwin sighed.

"Keep your wheels crossed, Olwin!" said Vee.

Morgan spent hours looking in the old parts shed.

"I'm afraid I've found everything but a firebox, Pete," Morgan told the old chugger.

"Well at least we tried. Thanks everyone," Pete said sadly.

As they all chugged home, Pete saw some pretty flowers at a small station. Suddenly he noticed the flowers were planted in a firebox!

"Stop! Firebox!" he yelled.

Later that day, Puffer Pete steamed out of the repair shed tooting his horn in delight.

"I've got my puff back!"

"Go Puffer Pete!" the trainees cheered as he chugged around the depot happily.

"GO PUFFER PETE!"

Goodnight chuggers

SWEET DREAMS

Answers

Page 9

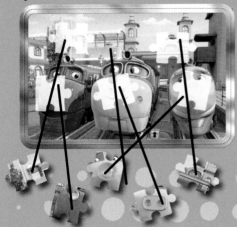

Page 12
10 chuggers

Page 13
Picture 3

Page 20
Track 2

Page 25
1 - B, 2 - B, 3 - A, 4 - A

Page 29
Hodge is the smallest
Mtambo is the largest

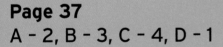

Page 37
A - 2, B - 3, C - 4, D - 1

Page 38
1 - A
2 - B
3 - B

Page 40
Grass - 2, Rubbish - 1
Wood - 5, Rocks - 4
Paper - 3, Metal - 6

Page 41
Dunbar has 3 hoppers
Calley has 5 spanners
Mtambo has 4 tickets
Frostini has 6 ice creams

Page 47

Page 54
1 - Purple, 2 - Red, 3 - Green,
4 - Blue, 5 - Yellow

Page 55
Picture 3

Page 56

Answers

Page 57

Pages 60-61

Koko ⚪⚫ Wilson ⚫

Brewster ⚪⚫ Olwin ⚫

Old Puffer Pete ⚫⚫ Calley ⚪

Pages 62-63
C and D match

Page 65
1 - elephant, 2 - lizard
3 - monkeys, 4 - giraffe

Page 72
10 monkeys

Page 73
Picture 3

Page 76

Page 77
Koko is first, Wilson is second,
Brewster is third

Pages 78 - 79

Page 83
Chugga, chugga, choo, choo!
Rattling rivets!
Absotootly amazing!

More chuggtastic books to collect!

Complete your Chuggington collection.
Tick them off as you collect!

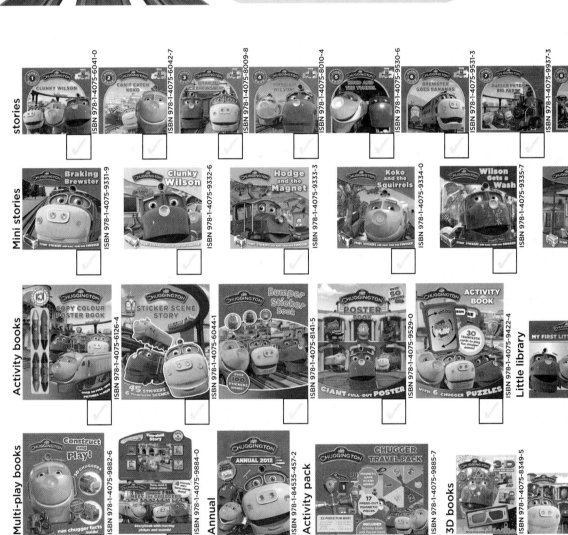

stories
- ISBN 978-1-4075-6041-0 — CLUNKY WILSON
- ISBN 978-1-4075-6042-7 — CAN'T CATCH KOKO
- ISBN 978-1-4075-8009-8 — BRAKING BREWSTER
- ISBN 978-1-4075-8010-4 — WIPEOUT WILSON
- ISBN 978-1-4075-9530-6 — HODGE AND THE TUNNEL
- ISBN 978-1-4075-9531-3 — BREWSTER GOES BANANAS
- ISBN 978-1-4075-9937-3 — PUFFER PETE'S BIG PARTY
- ISBN 978-1-4075-9938-0 — JETPACK WILSON

Mini stories
- ISBN 978-1-4075-9331-9 — Braking Brewster
- ISBN 978-1-4075-9332-6 — Clunky Wilson
- ISBN 978-1-4075-9333-3 — Hodge and the Magnet
- ISBN 978-1-4075-9334-0 — Koko and the Squirrels
- ISBN 978-1-4075-9335-7 — Wilson Gets a Wash
- ISBN 978-1-4075-9336-4 — Zephie's Zoomaround

Activity books
- ISBN 978-1-4075-6126-4 — COPY COLOUR POSTER BOOK
- ISBN 978-1-4075-6044-1 — STICKER SCENE STORY
- ISBN 978-1-4075-8141-5 — Bumper Sticker Book
- ISBN 978-1-4075-9529-0 — POSTER BOOK
- ISBN 978-1-4075-9422-4 — ACTIVITY BOOK

Little library
- ISBN 978-1-4075-6043-4 — MY FIRST LITTLE LIBRARY

Multi-play books
- ISBN 978-1-4075-9882-6 — Construct and Play!
- ISBN 978-1-4075-9884-0 — Time-aloud Story

Annual
- ISBN 978-1-84535-457-2 — ANNUAL 2012

Activity pack
- ISBN 978-1-4075-9885-7 — CHUGGER TRAVEL PACK

3D books
- ISBN 978-1-4075-8349-5 — 3D
- ISBN 978-1-4075-9780-5 — Chugger Sticker Colouring Pad

Play books
- ISBN 978-1-4075-6127-1 — SING AND LEARN
- ISBN 978-1-4075-8142-2 — KOKO ON CALL

Story collection
- ISBN 978-1-4075-6046-5 — Storybook Collection

Train books
- ISBN 978-1-4075-8138-5 — WILSON LET'S RIDE THE RAILS!
- ISBN 978-1-4075-8139-2 — KOKO CHUGGA CHUGGA CHOO CHOO!
- ISBN 978-1-4075-8140-8 — BREWSTER HONKING HORNS!
- ISBN 978-1-4075-9784-3 — I'M NUMBER ONE!